BIBLE PUZZLERS

by Carol Molski
Illustrated by Ed Koehler

CONCORDIA PUBLISHING HOUSE • SAINT LOUIS

To Kurt, Cassie, and Courtney.
Thank you so much for all of your
support and help. I am truly blessed
to have you as my family.

Copyright © 2007 Concordia Publishing House
3558 S. Jefferson Avenue
St. Louis, MO 63118-3968
1-800-325-3040 • www.cph.org

Written by Carol Molski
Illustrated by Ed Koehler

Manufactured in the United States of America

1 2 3 4 5 6 7 8 9 10   16 15 14 13 12 11 10 09 08 07

Contents

Introduction

Dear Parents and Teachers,

I am so excited that you have chosen to use *Bible Puzzlers!* Puzzles are a great way to "stretch" a child's mind. They can motivate a child to extend his logical thinking skills without even realizing it is happening. *Bible Puzzlers* will give your child an opportunity to think creatively, work on logical thinking skills, reinforce math and reading skills, and most important . . . learn more about God's Word in the process. What a wonderful opportunity to build on Bible literacy!

This book is filled with a wide variety of puzzles that will appeal to children in grades four through eight. Perhaps you are looking for something to help your class learn the books of the Bible. Or maybe you want to expose your child to a specific Bible story, passage, or theme. *Bible Puzzlers* is a great way to accomplish these goals. These puzzles can be used to supplement your religion curriculum and to give students additional exposure to God's Word after their other work is completed.

There is something for everyone in this book. But as teachers and parents, please keep a few things in mind as you use it. Make sure you choose a puzzle that will challenge your child without frustrating him. Consider dividing the class into groups and have them work on different puzzles. Perhaps you could have copies of puzzles available as self-directed activities or extra credit worksheets. The important thing to remember is to spend some time talking about the message of the puzzle once it is completed. Use these puzzles to encourage your child to explore the Bible and get to know the stories, people, and passages that bring joy and meaning to all of us. Celebrate the glory of God's Word!

Blessings,

Carol Molski

P.S. The answer key begins on page 56.

Fun with Names

Think of all the people who are mentioned in the Bible. Now, use your imagination and your sense of humor to identify the Bible character in each of the clues below. The first one has been done to help you get started.

1. Who made a lot of pictures? _Andrew_

2. What does a person do to the lawn?_____

3. What is a tiny particle in space? _____

4. If you can do something, you are what?_____

5. What do lame people sometimes need to walk?_____

6. What would you call a spot on the floor?_____

7. What would you call the right amount of something? _____

8. What did the female lamb do? _____

9. What is a very pretty shiny rock? _____

10. What do you do when the doctor puts a tongue depressor in your mouth? _____

11. What do you do when you need to get an answer from the teacher?_____

12. What do you use on a wrinkly shirt? _____

Word List

Aaron	Isaac
Abel	Isaiah
Adam	Mark
~~Andrew~~	Micah
Cain	Moses
Esther	Sheba

What's Your Name?

Many people have a nickname. A girl who is small for her age might be called Shortstuff. A boy who loves to ride his bike fast might be called Whiz. Imagine if famous biblical people had nicknames. Try to identify each of the people below by his or her nickname. Match the person to the nickname that best fits her or him.

1. **Rockhead** ____
2. **#1 Son** ____
3. **Traitor** ____
4. **Doubter** ____
5. **H₂O** ____
6. **Rooster** ____
7. **Big Ten** ____
8. **Hotshot** ____
9. **Working Woman** ____
10. **Chosen One** ____
11. **Beasty Boy** ____
12. **Water Boy** ____
13. **Fiery** ____
14. **Rainbow** ____
15. **#1** ____
16. **Ribsy** ____

a. **Moses**
b. **Jonah**
c. **Noah**
d. **Mary**
e. **Judas**
f. **Adam**
g. **Goliath**
h. **Joseph**
i. **Thomas**
j. **Daniel**
k. **Jesus**
l. **Peter**
m. **David**
n. **Eve**
o. **Meshach**
p. **Martha**

Which Is It?

The first column gives a one- or two-word clue. The second column gives a group of three people or things. Circle the word in the second column that best answers the clue. Use your knowledge of people, places, and things in the Bible to complete this puzzle.

Clue	Answer		
1. Disciple	Matthew	Mark	Moses
2. Naomi	Elizabeth	Ruth	Rebekah
3. Cain	Lot	Noah	Abel
4. Noah	Shimei	Ham	Jacob
5. Moses	Miriam	John	Herod
6. Abraham	Ezekiel	Jacob	Isaac
7. Mary	Martha	Naomi	Ruth
8. Bethany	Crucifixion	Baptism	Temptations
9. Mount Ararat	Ark	Tablets	Cross
10. Golgotha	Crucifixion	Wedding	Last Supper
11. Last Supper	Bread	Cheese	Water
12. Meshach	Herod	Abraham	Nebuchadnezzar
13. Red Sea	Noah	Moses	Abraham
14. Elizabeth	Martha	Rebekah	Mary
15. Gifts	Silver	Gold	Jewels

Famous Places

All the stories in the Bible happened to real people who lived in real places. Using your knowledge of Bible places, match the clues and the word list to complete this crossword puzzle.

Across
1. A quiet place to pray
3. Water into wine
5. Site of three crosses
8. Jesus ascends into heaven
9. The Promised Land
10. The crucifixion
11. Tumbling walls
12. A miracle on water

Down
1. Beginning of creation
2. Where Jesus spent His boyhood
4. Land of many tongues
6. The greatest birthplace
7. Jesus heals Peter's mother-in-law

Word List

Cana	Nazareth
Mt. of Olives	Bethlehem
Gethsemane	Capernaum
Sea of Galilee	Garden of Eden
Canaan	Jericho
Babel	Jerusalem
Golgotha	

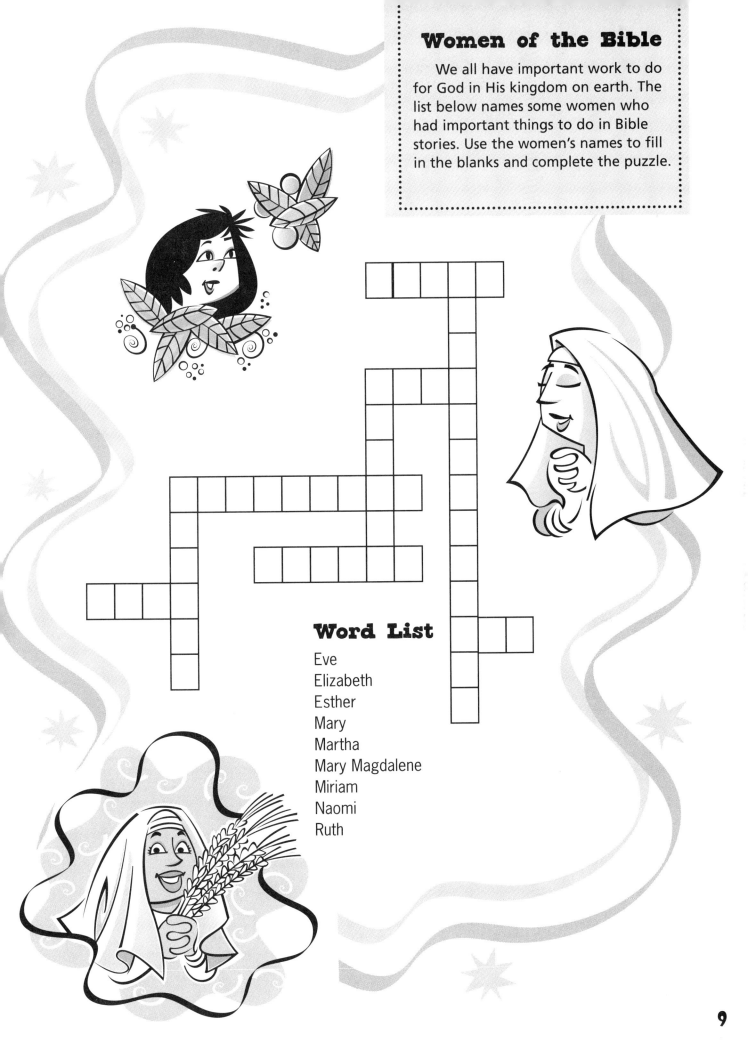

Women of the Bible

We all have important work to do for God in His kingdom on earth. The list below names some women who had important things to do in Bible stories. Use the women's names to fill in the blanks and complete the puzzle.

Word List

Eve
Elizabeth
Esther
Mary
Martha
Mary Magdalene
Miriam
Naomi
Ruth

9

Hidden Disciples

The names of eleven of the disciples are listed below. Circle the disciples' names in the word search. After you've found all the names, write the remaining letters from left to right in the spaces below to find out what Jesus said to His disciples.

W	A	L	L	A	U	T	W	H	P	O	R	I	T	Y
T	E	I	N	H	E	A	E	V	E	E	N	A	N	D
S	H	H	O	N	E	A	M	N	T	R	T	H	H	A
S	E	O	T	B	E	E	O	O	E	N	G	I	V	P
E	N	M	M	T	T	O	L	M	R	M	E	T	I	T
H	E	R	A	A	A	E	O	I	F	O	H	L	R	E
G	O	A	N	J	S	M	H	S	D	A	I	M	A	K
E	D	I	S	C	I	P	T	L	D	H	E	S	O	F
A	L	L	N	A	T	I	R	D	P	O	N	S	B	A
P	T	I	Z	I	N	G	A	T	A	H	E	M	I	N
T	H	E	N	A	M	E	B	N	N	E	O	F	T	H
E	F	A	T	H	U	E	D	H	R	A	N	D	O	F
T	H	E	S	S	O	R	O	N	A	N	D	O	F	T
H	E	H	O	L	E	J	Y	S	S	A	D	U	J	P
I	R	I	T	W	J	E	S	U	S	S	P	O	K	E

Word List

Andrew
Bartholomew
James
John

Judas
Matthew
Peter
Philip

Simon
Thaddaeus
Thomas

"___ _____ __ _____ ___ __
_____ ___ ____ _____ __ __.
_____ __ ___ ____ _____
__ ___ _____, _____ ____ __
___ ___ ___ _____ ___ __ ___
___ __ __ ___ ____ _____,"
[_ _ _ _ _ Hidden_].

10

There are 66 books in the Bible and many of them end with the letter S. Circle all the Bible books you can find in the word search. Use the word list below to help.

```
S N B V U R L Y N S H S S L K N S B T L
Y N Z S O H Q A N A N G E P W U M J M Z
Y W A Y E U Z A I O Z V T H Q M L T Q T
T Q K I B G I A I I I X S I D B A L F X
T G U K N S D T H T U L A L S E S T J M
X I J X E O A U I W X F I I N R P D E H
Z Y T H J T L T J B H T S P A S D H Y B
V V P U N S C A Q V A D E P I W T J S J
U E B E S U S O S I P B L I T H S I M Y
Q M M Q S N R N R S J M C A A Y E V N P
I A S U D O X E A I E G C N L S K P M X
L P R O V E R B S I N H E S A X B L A X
S O N G O F S O N G S T T N G P P J Q U
S E L C I N O R H C A S H U E A J A Y J
V R C B T E A E E M Y S O I F S J M E D
S T C A N J B O O T N I Y L A B I E W P
K I N G S R T S Y A O O S T O N L S L T
B S M Q E T S E M I K A Z H T C S F S I
W J Z W L R D O C F X N U T F S K S A B
A F S X T J R A D F Q S X R G Z Z H E C
```

Word List

Acts	Ephesians	Judges	Proverbs
Amos	Exodus	Kings	Psalms
Chronicles	Galatians	Lamentations	Romans
Colossians	Genesis	Leviticus	Song of Songs
Corinthians	Hebrews	Numbers	Thessalonians
Ecclesiastes	James	Philippians	Titus

Books of the Bible

In each row below is hidden the name of a book of the Bible. However, one letter in the name is missing. Insert a letter of the alphabet into each of the 24 empty boxes to reveal the names. The letter you insert may be at the beginning, the end, or in the middle of the word. Each letter of the alphabet will be used only once (you will not use the letters Q or F). Cross off each letter in the list as you use it.

HINT: The names have four or more letters; all the letters in the row are not necessarily used in forming the word. The first one is done for you.

A B C D E G H I J K L M N O P R S T U V W X Y Z

O	F	E	N	E	L	E	X	O	D	U	S	O	N	I
K	C	H	A	B	A	K		U	K	A	R	M	C	D
S	K	U	N	M	A	J		O	E	L	U	K	A	S
B	M	A	R	O	M	I		A	H	E	R	S	T	M
W	D	O	T	T	M	A		A	C	H	I	N	N	E
T	A	B	A	C	T	I		U	S	A	M	U	L	R
J	O	T	H	O	S	E		Z	R	A	K	E	W	A
R	T	I	M	E	S	T		E	R	U	T	I	P	T
A	P	E	L	I	J	U		G	E	S	R	O	N	L
L	H	E	B	E	L	P		O	V	E	R	B	S	Q
I	N	A	H	I	M	O		A	D	I	A	H	E	B
C	E	Z	E	K	L	E		I	T	I	C	U	S	U
E	J	A	M	O	P	H		L	E	M	O	N	E	H
E	T	I	M	O	T	H		E	M	O	Y	E	W	N
H	S	H	E	B	R	E		S	O	R	T	H	X	K
P	S	P	H	I	L	I		P	I	A	N	S	T	C
M	R	O	M	A	C	T		P	R	I	T	E	N	V
D	P	E	L	I	J	A		E	S	K	U	V	Z	O
U	A	V	M	A	R	E		R	A	M	E	S	T	F
Q	J	U	E	N	A	H		M	A	R	C	U	D	X
F	A	M	I	C	H	A		G	A	I	L	I	E	W
V	J	U	D	G	O	D		Z	E	K	I	E	L	P
N	T	I	M	O	T	J		H	N	O	A	T	E	G
G	C	H	R	O	M	A		S	T	R	O	N	T	J

People of the Bible

In each row below is hidden the name of a person who is mentioned in the Bible. However, one letter in the person's name is missing. Insert a letter of the alphabet into each of the 26 empty boxes to reveal the names. The letter you insert may be at the beginning, the end, or in the middle of the word. Each letter of the alphabet will be used only once. Cross off each letter in the list as you use it.

HINT: The names have four or more letters; all the letters in the row are not necessarily used in forming the word. The first one is done for you.

A B C D E F G H I J K L M N O P Q R S T U V W X Y Z

O	G	A	J	C	M	A	B	R	A	H	A	M	A	D	U	M	N	C
E	Y	F	U	M	A	R	E	L	I	A	H	J	O	E	S	P	H	
H	O	K	M	W	N	O	R	D	A	I	D	A	M	O	U	S	E	
V	P	V	B	S	T	U	J	O	S	M	E	O	N	T	I	N	T	
A	N	L	E	J	O	S	H	P	E	E	R	N	A	R	U	T	H	
F	V	O	W	A	B	E	D	N	E	O	L	I	A	T	H	O	V	
W	K	W	M	S	O	L	S	A	M	O	N	A	O	M	T	W	E	
Q	G	C	P	E	L	N	J	I	S	A	C	Z	E	A	R	N	A	
D	B	D	X	J	E	S	N	J	A	O	B	U	R	T	V	E	L	
L	A	V	N	B	E	N	J	M	A	T	H	A	M	T	H	E	N	
H	X	L	D	W	E	A	X	E	R	E	S	Z	I	N	K	L	I	
I	C	O	C	A	N	J	O	S	E	H	E	N	I	P	D	I	C	
Z	P	K	Y	D	A	U	R	N	C	U	I	R	I	N	I	U	S	
I	M	E	N	U	M	I	S	S	O	O	M	O	N	I	V	E	N	
Q	R	G	P	Z	E	N	E	H	E	I	A	H	O	L	D	E	R	
A	R	Z	Q	E	L	I	E	Z	E	I	E	L	J	H	I	N	E	
D	K	B	F	A	R	A	B	A	M	A	T	H	E	R	O	M	I	
T	M	Q	U	L	A	R	M	A	R	O	M	E	C	D	O	R	M	
N	S	R	A	B	O	N	A	A	R	N	T	O	N	D	E	R	N	
J	E	G	H	V	E	A	B	E	A	A	M	A	S	C	U	A	R	
B	U	S	R	M	A	R	K	E	N	E	C	H	A	R	I	A	H	
F	I	R	H	A	B	E	D	N	B	N	J	A	M	I	N	E	R	
C	S	S	T	A	B	A	R	A	B	A	S	K	E	R	E	C	O	
U	J	I	J	S	A	D	A	R	I	S	O	N	O	F	L	O	N	
L	W	X	T	G	A	L	I	C	I	A	O	M	I	C	I	O	V	
B	A	R	T	H	O	L	O	M	E	O	M	E	T	R	E	N	E	

Pathfinder

Follow one continuous winding path from start (Y) to finish (M) to discover the hidden Bible verse. The first letter of each word in the Bible verse is circled. The last letter of one word is next to the circled first letter of the next. The number of letters in each word in the verse is under the answer blanks (reading left to right, line by line). The path does not cross itself, and no letter is used more than once. Not all of the letters in the diagram will be used.

HINT: Draw through the letters as you use them.

START **FINISH**

C	A	D	E	(Y)	M	D	S	A	O	R	U	F	E	M	Y
Q	P	R	L	A	O	U	K	(W)	E	D	G	C	I	L	V
N	I	G	S	G	S	I	R	V	O	L	(I)	R	U	A	F
E	E	(F)	Y	A	Z	L	G	L	E	T	S	U	N	S	M
T	H	C	I	(M)	L	B	A	A	(L)	(A)	P	H	(P)	O	C
(A)	N	E	L	R	O	W	M	E	V	L	M	T	A	U	R
O	N	H	B	K	(T)	P	N	R	(F)	O	D	(P)	L	M	E
Q	T	D	P	G	H	A	M	T	E	N	R	Y	O	V	A
U	H	W	(A)	(L)	Y	G	H	N	C	V	V	(M)	B	S	H
R	S	E	F	E	I	H	I	L	D	T	S	T	N	M	F

___ 4   ___ 4   ___ 2   ___ 1   ___ 4   ___ 2   ___ 2   ___ 4   ___ 3   ___ 1

___ 5   ___ 3   ___ 2   ___ 4   ___ 5 .   119:105

14

The Path to God

Follow one continuous winding path from start (M) to finish (M) to discover the hidden Bible verse. The first letter of each word in the Bible verse is circled. The last letter of one word is next to the circled first letter of the next. The number of letters in each word in the verse is given under the answer blanks (reading left to right, line by line). The path does not cross itself, and no letter is used more than once. Not all of the letters in the diagram will be used.

HINT: Draw through the letters as you use them.

START

N	J	(M)	O	R	N	F	R	D	L	E	S	B	R	V	T	G	P	Y
L	H	A	Y	C	I	O	B	M	(A)	D	E	O	U	H	M	W	F	O
E	L	M	(T)	H	E	(L)	K	M	N	N	G	Q	C	S	D	V	Q	H
J	A	I	H	X	L	B	I	G	D	S	R	(D)	I	S	V	T	I	F
M	K	J	E	A	O	(Y)	R	E	W	N	Y	N	C	T	N	A	R	Z
K	O	A	R	Z	U	N	F	P	U	C	E	(I)	E	W	R	E	W	H
V	K	U	E	Y	C	(W)	H	A	D	R	J	L	P	D	Q	S	F	S
L	H	B	T	Q	B	N	E	D	O	(A)	P	L	H	P	I	S	E	R
A	W	X	F	S	Z	D	N	Q	U	N	G	B	L	A	S	(P)	V	K
C	Y	X	Z	O	A	G	(Y)	O	A	R	J	G	M	S	E	L	U	T

FINISH

Answer blanks:

☐☐☐ ☐☐☐ ☐☐☐☐ ☐☐☐☐☐☐
　3　　　3　　　4　　　　6

☐☐☐ ☐☐☐☐ ☐☐☐ ☐☐☐ ☐☐
　3　　　4　　　3　　　3　　2

☐☐☐☐☐☐☐☐ . ☐☐☐☐☐ 20:1
　　　8　　　　　　　5

15

Turn a Verse

Beginning at the starting point indicated, find your way through the maze to discover the hidden Bible verse. The verse is revealed by following one continuous path. The last letter of one word is next to the first letter of the next. The path does not cross not cross itself, and no letter is used more than once.

START

```
S I N G L E D E Q U K C W S O N J Z F P O N F G U
E U G T O T H D A D A N E N E G I M H O G J Y N H
E T Q V L X E L O R B I T C G F H O L D H C K I E
V L A I P B L Z S A Z H E H R O C K P C Q T R P Y
E U C V S T P H F W S A W H X J M S T H G I B L Z
F D K A W N D E B X D G X D I N C U B I A D I Y M
F G S Z V B U T H K O I V R V E L O X N G S F E J
R F T X O F C N S E N E M A N M Y B L O K H Z P J
Y R Z W K A P Y J K S L Q I D O S R K M S I T R X
A Z U A O S G W E T A Q V D S C T H G I R S D U P
F B R Y A H M R A Y L M A D N A H K Z X Y W H X B
V E A U V L J H Y V O B N M C M E D S L E X F Y Q
P R W J E R Q I A R H G D Y N J R W H E F G D B I
G S C D W H W A W P S I H Q C M K O X T L C M J K
R V M T O J B Z L S Y R E J W F T Q K P I O W L N
L T U T R K E D S A I M A Z F E B R N G U O V C H
A D H E A P Z G O L E C R L Y E N J V L X M Z H W
T U D B U I W Z K V F U Q G O R H I M Q K N J O V
V S P Q N P V G N A T I O N F A O M P S A L M X V
```

END

_____

_____

_____

_____ 98:1

Bible Quiz

Take this Bible quiz to see what kind of Bible scholar you are. The subject of the quiz is famous Bible places. *(Example:* Babel. *Answer:* The place where men began to speak in many languages.) Each question at the **student level** is worth one point. Each question at the **graduate level** is worth two points, and each question at the **scholar level** is worth three points. How many points can you score?

Student Level

1. Bethlehem _____

2. Eden _____

3. Lions' den _____

Graduate Level

4. Red Sea _____

5. Gethsemane _____

6. Golgotha _____

Scholar Level

7. Mount Ararat _____

8. Mount Sinai _____

9. Jordan River _____

SCORE

_____

PEOPLE

P
H
A
R
O
A
H

E
L
I
Z
A
B
E
T
H

EASTER

BIBLE

PLACES

CHRISTMAS

THINGS

Find the Relationship

Test your knowledge of Bible stories and themes. Below are groups of three things. Each item in each group is related to a Bible story. What is their relationship? Write your answer in the space provided.

1. Jump from the tallest building, bread, water

_____

2. Bartholomew, Matthew, John

_____

3. Locusts, death, frogs

_____

4. Merciful, pure in heart, peacemakers

_____

5. Exodus, Nehemiah, Hosea

_____

6. Coat, well, brothers

_____

7. Cross, crown of thorns, whip

_____

8. Mark, John, Titus

_____

9. Water, Ararat, dove

_____

10. Red Sea, pharaoh, Israelites

_____

Apostle Stumpers

How well do you know the twelve apostles? Following are twelve questions about the twelve men Jesus called to learn from Him and to spread His Gospel to the rest of the world. Use the names of the apostles to answer the questions. Some names may be used more than once.

1. Which apostles were brothers? _____

2. Which apostle changed his name?_____

3. Which apostle betrayed Jesus? _____

4. Which apostle was a twin?_____

5. Which two apostles did Jesus call first? _____

6. Jesus healed the mother-in-law of which apostle? _____

7. Which apostle was a tax collector? _____

8. Which apostle tried to walk on the water? _____

9. Which apostles were with Jesus during the transfiguration? _____

_____

10. Which two apostles were sons of Zebedee? _____

11. Which apostle denied Jesus? _____

12. Which apostles went with Jesus to watch over Him in the Garden of

Gethsemane? _____

_____

What Time Is It?

This puzzle has two parts. **First**, use the clues to fill in the blanks with the name of a famous Bible character. **Second**, match the letters of each person's name to the blanks in the puzzle below. (Use the numbers under each letter as a guide.) The second part of the puzzle will give you a famous Bible verse about time.

1. I parted the Red Sea. $\underline{}_{4}\ \underline{O}_{10}\ \underline{}_{6}\ \underline{}_{2}\ \underline{}_{6}$

2. I betrayed Jesus. $\underline{}_{9}\ \underline{}_{1}\ \underline{}_{16}\ \underline{}_{20}\ \underline{}_{6}$

3. I spent the night with lions. $\underline{}_{16}\ \underline{}_{20}\ \underline{}_{13}\ \underline{}_{5}\ \underline{}_{2}\ \underline{}_{11}$

4. I am Jesus' mother. $\underline{}_{4}\ \underline{}_{20}\ \underline{}_{25}\ \underline{}_{3}$

5. I had a baby when I was a very old woman. $\underline{}_{2}\ \underline{}_{11}\ \underline{}_{5}\ \underline{}_{21}\ \underline{}_{20}\ \underline{}_{17}\ \underline{}_{2}\ \underline{}_{7}\ \underline{}_{12}$

6. I baptized Jesus. $\underline{}_{9}\ \underline{}_{10}\ \underline{}_{12}\ \underline{}_{13}\quad \underline{}_{7}\ \underline{}_{12}\ \underline{}_{2}\quad \underline{}_{17}\ \underline{}_{20}\ \underline{}_{8}\ \underline{}_{7}\ \underline{}_{5}\ \underline{}_{6}\ \underline{}_{7}$

7. My father was ready to use me as a sacrifice. $\underline{}_{5}\ \underline{}_{6}\ \underline{}_{20}\ \underline{}_{20}\ \underline{}_{14}$

8. I'm a giant of a man. $\underline{}_{15}\ \underline{}_{10}\ \underline{}_{11}\ \underline{}_{5}\ \underline{}_{20}\ \underline{}_{7}\ \underline{}_{12}$

9. I am God, but I am also called $\underline{}_{18}\ \underline{}_{20}\ \underline{}_{7}\ \underline{}_{12}\ \underline{}_{2}\ \underline{}_{25}$ or $\underline{}_{9}\ \underline{}_{2}\ \underline{}_{12}\ \underline{O}_{10}\ \underline{}_{22}\ \underline{}_{20}\ \underline{}_{12}$.

10. I am one of Jesus' disciples. $\underline{}_{20}\ \underline{}_{13}\ \underline{}_{16}\ \underline{}_{25}\ \underline{}_{2}\ \underline{}_{19}$

$\underline{}_{7}\ \underline{}_{12}\ \underline{}_{2}\ \underline{}_{25}\ \underline{}_{2}\quad \underline{}_{5}\ \underline{}_{6}\quad \underline{}_{20}\quad \underline{}_{7}\ \underline{}_{5}\ \underline{}_{4}\ \underline{}_{2}\quad \underline{}_{18}\ \underline{O}_{10}\ \underline{}_{25}\quad \underline{}_{2}\ \underline{}_{22}\ \underline{}_{2}\ \underline{}_{25}\ \underline{}_{3}\ \underline{}_{7}\ \underline{}_{12}\ \underline{}_{5}\ \underline{}_{13}\ \underline{}_{15}$

$\underline{}_{20}\ \underline{}_{13}\ \underline{}_{16}\quad \underline{}_{20}\quad \underline{}_{6}\ \underline{}_{2}\ \underline{}_{20}\ \underline{}_{6}\ \underline{O}_{10}\ \underline{}_{13}\quad \underline{}_{18}\ \underline{}_{10}\ \underline{}_{25}\quad \underline{}_{2}\ \underline{}_{22}\ \underline{}_{2}\ \underline{}_{25}\ \underline{}_{3}$

$\underline{}_{20}\ \underline{}_{14}\ \underline{}_{7}\ \underline{}_{5}\ \underline{}_{22}\ \underline{}_{5}\ \underline{}_{7}\ \underline{}_{3}\quad \underline{}_{1}\ \underline{}_{13}\ \underline{}_{16}\ \underline{}_{2}\ \underline{}_{25}\quad \underline{}_{12}\ \underline{}_{2}\ \underline{}_{20}\ \underline{}_{22}\ \underline{}_{2}\ \underline{}_{13}$.

$\underline{}_{2}\ \underline{}_{14}\ \underline{}_{14}\ \underline{}_{11}\ \underline{}_{2}\ \underline{}_{6}\ \underline{}_{5}\ \underline{}_{20}\ \underline{}_{6}\ \underline{}_{7}\ \underline{}_{2}\ \underline{}_{6}$ 3: 1

HINT:
If you have trouble figuring out the Bible characters, fill in the letters you know from the rest of the puzzle.

When Did It Happen?

Put the following events from Jesus' life in the order they actually happened by placing the letter in its proper place, 1–21, to reveal a Bible verse. If you get stuck, look at a timeline in a Bible.

H – Jesus tells parables about the kingdom

U – The Last Supper

R – Jesus is baptized

O – Jesus walks on the water

O – Jesus appears on the road to Emmaus

W – Jesus is born

L – Jesus feeds 5000 people

Y – Jesus talks to Zacchaeus

H – Jesus turns water to wine

O – Jesus is presented in the temple

O – The triumphal entry

D – The ascension

R – The transfiguration

P – Jesus heals Peter's mother-in-law

G – The crucifixion

S – Jesus is tempted by Satan

E – Jesus calms the storm

D – Jesus raises Lazarus from the dead

R – Gethsemane

I – Jesus calls the first disciples

T – Sermon on the Mount

1. _____
2. _____
3. _____
4. _____
5. _____
6. _____
7. _____
8. _____
9. _____
10. _____
11. _____
12. _____
13. _____
14. _____
15. _____
16. _____
17. _____
18. _____
19. _____
20. _____
21. _____

" _____ "

— — — — — — — —   — — —   — — — —   — — — —   — — —. Luke 4:8

The following quotes are ones we often hear. Can you identify the Bible stories they are taken from? Use your Bible to look up the book, chapter, and verse.

1. "Why were you searching for Me? . . . Didn't you know I had to be in My Father's house?"

   _____

   _____

2. "I am the Lord's servant. . . . May it be to me as you have said."

   _____

   _____

3. "Come, follow Me."

   _____

   _____

4. "This is My body given for you; do this in remembrance of Me."

   _____

   _____

5. "If anyone wants to be first, he must be the very last, and the servant of all."

   _____

   _____

6. "Blessed are the poor in spirit, for theirs is the kingdom of heaven."

   _____

   _____

7. "You of little faith. . . . Why did you doubt?"

   _____

   _____

8. "My Father, if it is possible, may this cup be taken from Me. Yet not as I will, but as You will."

   _____

9. "Before the rooster crows, you will disown Me three times."

   _____

   _____

10. "Eloi, Eloi, lama sabachthani?"—which means, "My God, My God, why have You forsaken Me?"

    _____

    _____

11. "Therefore go and make disciples of all nations, baptizing them in the name of the Father and of the Son and of the Holy Spirit, and teaching them to obey everything I have commanded you."

    _____

    _____

12. "I am the resurrection and the life. He who believes in Me will live, even though he dies."

    _____

    _____

13. "Father, forgive them, for they do not know what they are doing."

    _____

    _____

14. "Man does not live on bread alone."

    _____

    _____

15. "This will be a sign to you: You will find a baby wrapped in cloths and lying in a manger."

    _____

God's Word Is No Mystery

The code below uses symbols instead of letters to spell words. Match the symbols in the code to letters in the message. Write each letter on the line provided. You will discover a message from God's Word about who you are in His kingdom.

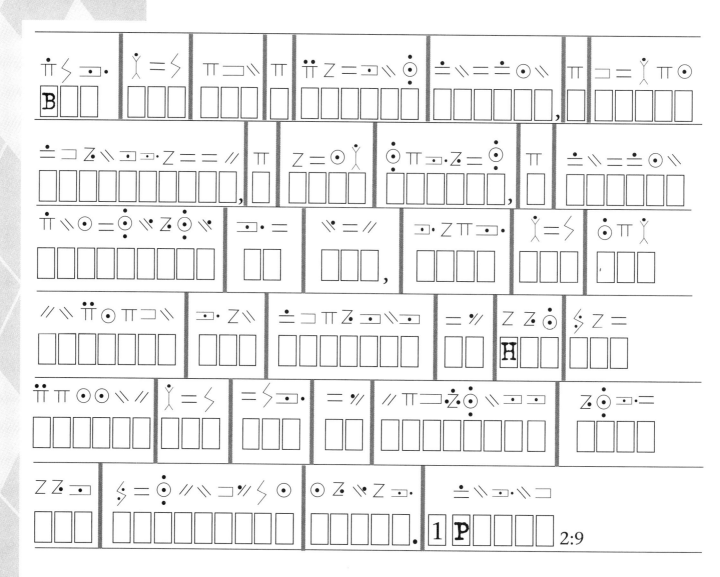

24

Simon Says

This puzzle requires a lot of concentration! Follow the directions carefully to discover the answer to the question at the bottom of the page. Workspace is provided.

HINT: Use a pencil!

Use the following words:

THROWN INTO A BLAZING FURNACE.

Delete the word ROW.
Delete the TH.
Delete the first 3 vowels.
Replace the second and third consonants with one E.
Have the L and the U exchange places.
Move the C between the U and the A.
Insert an H in the sixth position.
Exchange the I for a D.
Delete the third and fourth consonants from the end.
Move the Z between N and G.
Move the last vowel to the immediate left of the Z.
Replace the G with the last vowel.
Delete the last consonant.
Add a Z to the left of the other Z.

Who had Shadrach, Meshach, and Abednego thrown into a blazing furnace?

It's No Secret

We need something important in order to live. What is it? To solve this puzzle, answer each question below by circling a letter. Then, write each letter on the numbered lines it corresponds to below. The first one has been done for you.

1. If Jonah went to Nineveh, circle Ⓜ If not, circle O.
2. If Joseph put 18 gold pieces in Benjamin's sack, circle E. If not, circle D.
3. If David was the son of Jesse, circle A. If not, circle T.
4. If the ark landed on Mount Horeb, circle N. If not, circle O.
5. If Naomi was Ruth's mother, circle W. If not, circle T.
6. If Moses parted the Sea of Galilee, circle S. If not, circle E.
7. If Aaron was Moses' brother, circle N. If not, circle F.
8. If Jacob and Esau were twins, circle S. If not, circle U.
9. If God created the stars on the fifth day, circle G. If not, circle L.
10. If Samson had seven braids, circle B. If not, circle R.
11. If Judas was the first disciple called, circle I. If not, circle Y.
12. If John the Baptist was beheaded, circle V. If not, circle C.
13. If the shepherds were the first to hear the news of Christ's birth, circle R. If not, circle H.
14. If Matthew was a fisherman, circle Y. If not, circle U.
15. If Peter denied Jesus four times, circle L. If not, circle I.
16. If James was with Jesus during the transfiguration, circle W. If not, circle A.
17. If Moses married Zipporah, circle H. If not, circle D.
18. If God created the water animals on the sixth day, circle V. If not, circle C.
19. If Elizabeth was the mother of John the Baptist, circle F. If not, circle B.
20. If Simon Peter cut off the high priest's finger, circle M. If not, circle G.

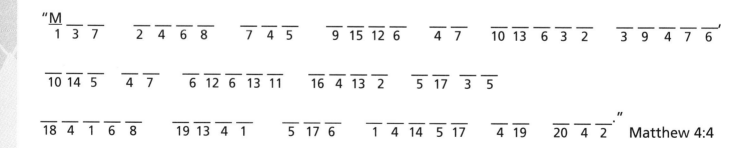

"M___ ___   ___ ___ ___ ___   ___ ___ ___   ___ ___ ___ ___   ___ ___   ___ ___ ___ ___ ___   ___ ___ ___ ___ ___'
  1 3 7   2 4 6 8   7 4 5   9 15 12 6   4 7   10 13 6 3 2   3 9 4 7 6

___ ___ ___   ___ ___   ___ ___ ___ ___ ___   ___ ___ ___ ___   ___ ___ ___ ___
 10 14 5   4 7   6 12 6 13 11   16 4 13 2   5 17 3 5

___ ___ ___ ___ ___   ___ ___ ___ ___   ___ ___ ___   ___ ___ ___ ___ ___   ___ ___   ___ ___ ___."
 18 4 1 6 8   19 13 4 1   5 17 6   1 4 14 5 17   4 19   20 4 2   Matthew 4:4

26

What's Left?

All of the words in the columns below are found in your Bible. But the answer to the puzzle doesn't use all of these words. To solve the puzzle, follow the directions carefully. When you are finished, the remaining words will form a Bible verse reading left to right, line by line. Some words may be eliminated by more than one of the instructions. Words that have been crossed out may be used to eliminate other words.

Cross out all words in columns C and D that are names of the disciples.

Cross out all words in all columns that are books of the Bible.

Cross out all words in columns B and C that are related to the Christmas story.

Cross out all words in column C that have the plural form in column D, and vice versa.

Cross out all words in columns A and D that are animal names.

Cross out all words in columns A and C that are homophones.

Cross out all words in columns A and B that are direction words.

Cross out all words in all columns that are names of biblical cities.

A	B	C	D
Daniel	trust	Peter	bushes
in	oxen	where	horse
Genesis	star	the	Bethlehem
wear	Hosea	bush	James
Lord	west	Simon	Joel
there	with	angel	promise
donkey	south	all	cow
north	Proverbs	promises	your
east	Cana	Matthew	Nazareth
Revelation	stable	their	heart

_____ __ ____ __ ___ _____ ____ ___ _____. Proverbs 3:5

Calling on Jesus

The Bible verse hidden in the puzzle below is in a number code based on the familiar telephone buttons. Each number represents one of the letters shown with it on the telephone button. You must decide which one. A number is not necessarily the same letter each time.

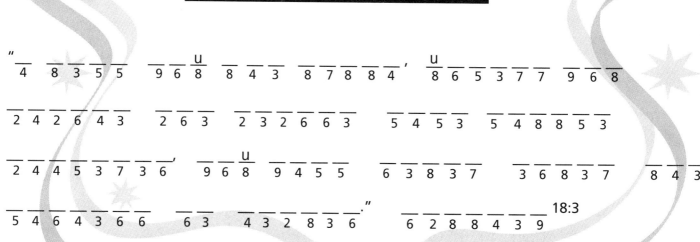

"__ __ __ __ __   __ __ __ __ __ __ __ __ __ __ __ ,   __ __ __ __ __ __ __ __ __
 4 8 3 5 5   9 6 8(u) 8 4 3   8 7 8 8 4   8(u)6 5 3 7 7   9 6 8

__ __ __ __ __ __ __ __ __ __ __ __ __ __ __ __ __ __ __ __ __ __ __ __ __
 2 4 2 6 4 3   2 6 3   2 3 2 6 6 3   5 4 5 3   5 4 8 8 5 3

__ __ __ __ __ __ __ __ , __ __ __ __ __ __ __ __ __ __ __ __ __ __ __ __ __ __ __ __
 2 4 4 5 3 7 3 6   9 6 (u) 9 4 5 5   6 3 8 3 7   3 6 8 3 7   8 4 3

__ __ __ __ __ __ __ __ __ __ __ __ __ __ __ ." __ __ __ __ __ __ __ 18:3
 5 4 6 4 3 6 6   6 3   4 3 2 8 3 6   6 2 8 8 4 3 9

Hello, Jesus?

The Bible verse hidden in the puzzle below is in a number code based on the familiar telephone buttons. Each number represents one of the letters shown with it on the telephone button. You must decide which one. A number is not necessarily the same letter each time.

"__ __ __ __ __ __ __   __ __ __   _y__ __ __   __ __ __   __ __ __   __ __ __ __,
  2 5 3 7 7 3 3   2 7 3   9 6 8   9 4 6   2 7 3   7 6 6 7

__ __ __   _y__ __ __ __ __   __ __   __ __ __   __ __ __ __ __ __ __
 3 6 7   9 6 8 7 7   4 7   8 4 3   5 4 6 4 3 6 6

__ __   __ __ __."   __ __ __ __ 6:20
 6 3   4 6 3   5 8 5 3

Three of a Kind

The name for a wonderful gift from God is hidden in the puzzle below. To find it, locate in the diagram all the letters that appear exactly alike three times. Rearrange the three-of-a-kind letters to spell the word that saves us all.

HINT: A letter may appear several times in different styles, but only those that are exact triplicates will spell the name of this gift.

A	W	E	G	R
C	J	F	D	U
R	A	N	Q	A
G	B	S	M	G
E	B	A	J	R
W	Z	G	V	I
I	U	G	C	E
R	K	S	G	W
E	T	S	X	G
I	T	C	Q	E

Three of a kind word: ____________________

Biblical Equations

Each equation below contains a number and the first letter of words that will make it complete. Fill in the missing words to complete the puzzle. Here is an example: 40 = D and N in the D is "Days and Nights in the Desert."

1. 12 = A_____ for J_____

2. 40 = D_____ and N_____ of R_____

3. 3 = C _____on G_____

4. 2 = of E_____ K_____ of A_____ on the A_____

5. 3 = D_____ traveled while M_____and J_____ searched for J_____

6. 7 = D_____ of C _____

7. 7 = T_____ the I_____ M_____ around the C_____

8. 7 = C_____ of R_____

9. 10 = P_____ on the E_____

10. 10 = C_____ on the T_____

Bits and Pieces

Test your Bible knowledge with this puzzle. Can you identify these famous Bible "pairs" from the bits and pieces shown in the boxes? Use your Bible for clues if you have trouble.

VID OLI	**Answer:** David and Goliath
UTH AOM	
MSO LAH	
ARY ART	
JAC ESA	
AIN ABE	
MAR SEP	
ARO SES	
ETE OHN	
AUL SIL	
RAH ARA	
ANI IUS	
ARA MOS	
JON HAL	
ISH LIJ	

You've learned a lot about Jesus' life on earth. Use your Bible knowledge and these rebus clues to help you make a timeline of some of the major events in the life of Christ.

1. 🪞 – ror + [A ♦ A] – e + [3 < 8] – s _____

2. 🪂 – chute + 💪 – ed + s _____

3. 🐦 – d + 🌹 – orn _____

4. 1st 2 3 4 🍽️ _____

5. 📈 – d + 😙🎵 – ng + on _____

6. 🚄 + s + 🥊 – ht + ☄️ – nus + tion _____

7. 🏃 – tch + 🏙️ – ty + 🚗 + ion _____

8. ⛪ – le. + 💪 – oo + ion _____

9. 💎 – m + h + 🦭 – al + 🐴 _____

10. ⚾ – ll + p + 🤧 – sue + m _____

11. 😴 – t + ur + ◉ – ord + tion _____

33

Picture Books

How many books of the Bible are there? How many of them can you name? Use these rebus clues to help you identify some of them. If you have trouble, open your Bible to the Table of Contents and complete the puzzle.

1. [WELCOME] + [NOW SHOWING] - ater + w _____

2. [peanut] - t + m + [bee] - e + rs _____

3. [EXIT] - it + o + [duck] - ck + s _____

4. [pin] - tk + [foot] - oe _____

5. [arm] - int + [bush] - rb + a _____

6. [map] p + [broom sweeping] - ae _____

7. [genie lamp] - i + [family] - ter _____

8. [knight jousting] - ust + [bird nest] - e _____

9. [corn] - n + [OUT] + [leg] - gh + [ants] - t _____

10. [devil] - vil + [boat] - bt + 1 - e + o + [monkey] - onke _____

11. [lungs] - ng + [key] - y _____

12. [joystick] - er + [chair] - s + i + [scissors] - t + s _____

Sudoku puzzles are fun and challenging. Use the clues provided to complete this sudoku-style puzzle. Fill in each square with a number so when the numbers are added across or down, the result is the answer to the question at the end of the row or column.

30		2		Days Jesus was in the desert
			1	Number of commandments
2	1			Days of creation
	2	2		Disciples of Jesus

Rainy days on the ark	Number of plagues	Churches of Revelation	Number of letters in victoriously

35

Proverb Wheel 1

This puzzle has two steps. **First,** find the missing word for each Bible verse below. To do this, look at the Proverb Wheel and find the small inner wheel marked "1." Three letters of the missing word are given on this wheel. Fill in the remaining letters to complete the word needed for the Bible verse. Then do the same for the rest of the verses.

Second, place the letters you added to the small inner wheels in the adjoining spaces in the outer wheel. You may need to unscramble them first to make words. Start at the arrow and read clockwise. The hidden verse from Proverbs is revealed and the puzzle is complete!

1. "Watch out for false prophets. They come to you in _____ clothing, but inwardly they are ferocious wolves." Matthew 7:15

2. "Now My heart is troubled, and what shall I say? 'Father, save Me from this hour'? No, it was for this very _____ I came to this hour." John 12:27

3. Lord, by such things men live; and my spirit finds life in them too. You restored me to _____ and let me live. Isaiah 38:16

4. Your statutes stand firm; holiness _____ Your house for endless days, O LORD. Psalms 93:5

5. _____ in me a pure heart, O God, and renew a steadfast spirit within me. Psalm 51:10

6. "Heal the sick, raise the dead, cleanse those who have leprosy, drive out demons. Freely you have received, _____ give." Matthew 10:8

7. You were anointed as a guardian _____ , for so I ordained you. You were on the holy mount of God; you walked among the fiery stones. Ezekiel 28:14

8. "The Son of Man came eating and drinking, and they say, 'Here is a glutton and a drunkard, a friend of tax collectors and "sinners."' But wisdom is _____ right by her actions." Matthew 11:19

9. The LORD God formed the man from the dust of the ground and breathed into his nostrils the _____ of life, and the man became a living being. Genesis 2:7

START

PROVERB WHEEL

Proverb Wheel 2

This puzzle has two steps. **First,** find the missing word for each Bible verse below. To do this, look at the Proverb Wheel and find the small inner wheel marked "1." Three letters of the missing word are given on this wheel. Fill in the remaining letters to complete the word needed for the Bible verse. Then do the same for the rest of the verses.

Second, place the letters you added to the small inner wheels in the adjoining spaces in the outer wheel. You may need to unscramble them first to make words. Start at the arrow and read clockwise. The hidden verse from Proverbs is revealed and the puzzle is complete!

1. Cleanse me with hyssop, and I will be clean; wash me, and I will be _____ than snow. Psalm 51:7

2. In the paths of the wicked lie thorns and snares, but he who _____ his soul stays far from them. Proverbs 22:5

3. I am sending you out like sheep among wolves. Therefore be as _____ as snakes and as innocent as doves. Matthew 10:16

4. "My sheep _____ to My voice; I know them, and they follow Me." John 10:27

5. He restores my soul. He _____ me in paths of righteousness for His name's sake. Psalm 23:3

6. For wisdom is more precious than rubies, and nothing you _____ can compare with her. Proverbs 8:11

7. A good name is more desirable than great riches; to be esteemed is better than _____ or gold. Proverbs 22:1

8. Beware of turning to evil, which you seem to _____ to affliction. Job 36:21

9. People will be _____ of themselves, _____ of money, boastful, proud, abusive, disobedient to their parents, ungrateful, unholy. 2 Timothy 3:2

START

PROVERB WHEEL

37

What's Missing?

Each of the words below is the name of a person who is mentioned in the Bible. Fill in the missing vowels for the names. Then count how many of each vowel you used and write that number in the correct space below. Finally, add all these numbers to answer the question at the bottom of the page.

1. M __ S __ S
2. N __ __ H
3. D __ N __ __ L
4. M __ RY
5. __ D __ M
6. __ V __
7. S __ M __ __ L
8. J __ S __ PH
9. J __ S __ S
10. D __ V __ D
11. __ L __ J __ H
12. R __ TH
13. N __ __ M __
14. S __ L __ M __ N
15. __ BR __ H __ M
16. __ S __ __ C
17. __ NDR __ W

Total number of O's _____   Total number of A's _____

Total number of U's _____   Total number of E's _____

Total number of I's _____

Add all of the vowels to answer this question: How many

books are in the Old Testament? _____

Where Am I?

All of the stories in the Bible took place in real cities and countries. This puzzle gives you the names of some of the places that are identified in the Bible. To find the names, fill in the blanks to complete words that read across. The letters you fill in will spell the name of a Bible city or country when read from top to bottom. The first letter is filled in to help you get started. If you're not sure of the spelling, look at the index in your Bible or at a Bible dictionary.

1.
```
S  I  G  H
M  E  _  T
H  E  _  M
S  H  _  N
M  E  _  T
S  E  _  N
F  E  _  L
```

2.
```
O  B  _  E  C  T
C  R  _  T  E
B  O  _  R  O  W
T  R  _  P  O  D
D  E  _  I  D  E
S  C  _  O  O  L
B  R  _  K  E  N
```

3.
```
A  _  A  R
B  _  A  N
D  _  U  M
M  _  S  T
I  _  N' T
B  _  L  L
S  _  A  M
B  _  A  N
A  _  E  N
```

4.
```
N  I  _  B  L  E
F  R  _  E  Z  E
B  O  _  T  L  E
S  C  _  O  O  L
F  A  _  L  E  N
B  R  _  A  T  H
S  C  _  E  M  E
T  R  _  A  T  Y
D  A  _  A  G  E
```

5.
```
A  _  L  E
M  _  N  E
A  _  E  D
L  _  R  E
S  _  E  D
M  _  O  N
O  _  T  O
```

6.
```
B  A  L  _  A  M
S  O  L  _  C  E
F  A  R  _  E  R
I  N  T  _  C  T
S  O  R  _  O  W
F  A  M  _  S  H
A  T  T  _  C  K
```

7.
```
B  R  A  _  D
C  R  E  _  M
C  R  A  _  Y
D  R  E  _  M
C  A  R  _  Y
K  N  E  _  L
F  I  F  _  H
N  I  G  _  T
```

8.
```
H  A  N  _  L  E  R
D  R  E  _  M  E  R
D  R  U  _  M  E  R
H  U  M  _  N  L  Y
G  L  A  _  S  E  S
S  U  C  _  E  S  S
T  R  O  _  B  L  E
F  R  E  _  H  E  N
```

9.
```
B  A  _  O  N
S  H  _  M  E
F  E  _  C  E
S  T  _  I  N
```

10.
```
G  R  _  A  T
W  O  _  E  N
L  E  _  O  N
T  R  _  C  E
L  A  _  G  H
M  O  _  S  Y
```

39

Who Am I?

All of the people you read about in the Bible really lived. This puzzle gives you the names of some of the people who are identified in the Bible. To find the names, fill in the blanks to complete words that read across. The letters you fill in will spell the name of a Bible person when read from top to bottom. Some letters are filled in to help you get started. If you're not sure of the spelling, look at the index in your Bible or at a Bible dictionary.

1. L O N _ O N
   B A N _ N A
   H E A _ E N
   L O V _ N G
   G A R _ E N

2. A _ A I N
   H _ U N D S
   G _ A S S
   F _ N D S
   R _ N C H
   S _ O N E
   T _ O S E

3. M _ D E
   I _ E A
   S _ M E
   O _ E N

4. S H _ L L S
   S A _ I N G
   T H _ I R S

5. S T _ E E T
   T H _ M B S
   K E _ T L E
   R E _ E A T

6. H A M _ E R
   E N F _ L D
   H A S _ L E
   F R I _ N D
   R A I _ N

7. I _ P U T
   C _ N E S
   F _ N C Y
   S _ A L L

8. M A _ O R
   S M _ L L
   F I _ T S
   S L _ M S
   M I _ T Y

9. H A _ P E N
   T H _ O R Y
   L E _ T E R
   C H _ C K S
   C I _ C U S

10. M A _ O R
    T R _ C E
    M E _ A L
    C R _ W L
    H A _ T E

11. H A _ D
    C L _ N
    L I _ N
    N A _ E
    P A _ R

12. W _ I R D
    A _ T E R
    S _ A R E
    C _ O R E
    B _ N C H
    T _ A I N

Put Them All Together and What Have You Got?

Choose one syllable from column A, one from B, and one from C to form a book of the Bible. Each syllable in each column may be used only once. Write the new words in column D.

Hint: Cross out the syllables as you use them.

A+B+C=D

Column A	Column B	Column C	Column D
Ge	la	a	_____
Ga	mo	ah	_____
Josh	se	chi	_____
Ha	los	sis	_____
Ex	phe	mon	_____
I	o	kuk	_____
Phi	u	sians	_____
Ho	ne	cles	_____
Chro	bak	dus	_____
Mal	sai	a	_____
E	ni	tians	_____
Co	a	thy	_____
Ti	le	sians	_____

Six-Letter Words

In each of the squares below is the second half of a six-letter word or name related to the Bible. The first half of each word is listed below. Can you match these halves to form 24 words? The first has been done for you.

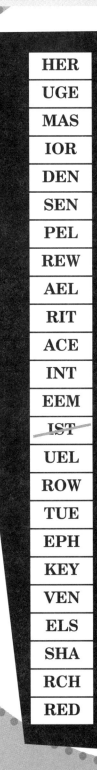

HER
UGE
MAS
IOR
DEN
SEN
PEL
REW
AEL
RIT
ACE
INT
EEM
~~**IST**~~
UEL
ROW
TUE
EPH
KEY
VEN
ELS
SHA
RCH
RED

1. Chr _ist_____
2. Gar_____
3. Don_____
4. Fat_____
5. Ang_____
6. And_____
7. Ano_____
8. Chu_____
9. Cho_____
10. Eli_____
11. Gos_____
12. Hea_____
13. Isr_____
14. Jos_____
15. Pal_____
16. Red_____
17. Ref_____
18. Sac_____
19. Sam_____
20. Sav_____
21. Sor_____
22. Spi_____
23. Tho_____
24. Vir_____

Disciples in Christ

A "disciple" is someone who believes that Jesus Christ is God the Son and our Savior from sin, and tells others about Him. How many words can you make from the letters in "Disciples in Christ"?

DISCIPLES IN CHRIST

_____   _____   _____

_____   _____   _____

_____   _____   _____

_____   _____   _____

_____   _____   _____

_____   _____   _____

_____   _____   _____

_____   _____   _____

_____   _____   _____

_____   _____   _____

_____   _____   _____

_____   _____   _____

_____   _____   _____

_____   _____   _____

Little Words from Big Words

Each of the following small words can be found within one of the names of the books of the Bible. Can you think of a book for each of the words? Do not use any book more than once. Some of the little words may have more than one answer. The first one has been done for you.

Hint: Use the table of contents in your Bible to check your answers.

OLD TESTAMENT

1. men La*men*tations
2. hem _____
3. us _____
4. her _____
5. verb _____
6. sea _____
7. hag _____
8. hum _____

NEW TESTAMENT

1. man _____
2. hew _____
3. moth _____
4. salon _____
5. lip _____
6. ark _____
7. loss _____
8. lemon _____
9. revel _____
10. he _____
11. am _____
12. brew _____

Mystery Code to Jesus' Life

Each of the code words below is an important event from Jesus' life on earth. Decipher the code to find the correct spelling of each event. The first one has been done for you.

Hint: Use the known letters in the first word to help decode other words.

A	B	C	D	E	F	G	H	I	J	K	L	M	N	O	P	Q	R	S	T	U	V	W	X	Y	Z
						T																			

1. GIZMHURTFIZGRLM   **Transfiguration**

2. OZHG HFKKVI   _ _ _ _ _ _ _ _ _ _

3. YRIGS   _ _ _ _ _

4. XIFXRURCRLM   _ _ _ _ _ _ _ _ _ _ _

5. YZKGRHN   _ _ _ _ _ _ _

6. GVNKGZGRLM   _ _ _ _ _ _ _ _ _ _

7. HVINLM LM GSV NLFMG   _ _ _ _ _ _ _ _ _ _ _ _ _ _ _ _

8. NRIZXOVH   _ _ _ _ _ _ _ _

9. KZIZYOVH   _ _ _ _ _ _ _ _

10. TVGSHVNZMV   _ _ _ _ _ _ _ _ _ _

11. IVHFIIVXGRLM   _ _ _ _ _ _ _ _ _ _ _ _

12. ZHXVMHRLM   _ _ _ _ _ _ _ _ _

45

Scrambled Books

Some of the books of the Old Testament are listed below, but they're in a scrambled mess! All of syllables are there, but they are in the wrong order. Unscramble the syllables to reveal the Old Testament books.

Hint: Use the table of contents in your Bible if you need help.

1. SE HO A _____

2. BA AH O DI _____

3. NE SIS GE _____

4. A MAL CHI _____

5. VI CUS LE TI _____

6. CHA AH ZE RI _____

7. O DEU ON TER MY _____

8. SAI I AH _____

9. ZE AH NI PHA _____

10. KI E EL ZE _____

11. HE AH NE MI _____

12. O DUS EX _____

13. U JOSH A _____

14. SI TES EC AS CLE _____

15. MI JER AH E _____

16. KUK BAK HA _____

17. LA TIONS TA MEN _____

And It Was Good

This is a two-part puzzle. First, unscramble each word in the list and write the letters in the correct order in the blanks. The letters inside the circles are the clues to the second part of the puzzle. Unscramble these letters to fill in the blanks at the bottom of the page. Then you will have the answer to question. If you need help, read the first chapter of the first book in the Old Testament.

1. ADY   _ _ ⃝

2. NAPLST   _ _ _ _ ⃝ _

3. RSATS   _ _ _ ⃝ _

4. AMN   _ ⃝ _

5. HINGT   _ _ _ _ ⃝

6. ONMO   _ _ ⃝ _

7. KSY   ⃝ _ _

8. AWNOM   _ ⃝ _ _ _

9. IALNMSA   _ ⃝ _ _ _ _ _

10. EEVHNAS   _ ⃝ _ _ _ _ _

11. USN   _ _ ⃝

12. TREHA   _ _ ⃝ _ _

13. NOCSAE   _ ⃝ _ _ _ _

What do all of these words have in common?

_ _ _ _ _ _ _ _   _ _ _ _

47

The Greatest Birth

This is a two-part puzzle. First, unscramble each word in the list and write the letters in the correct order in the blanks. The letters inside the circles are the clues to the second part of the puzzle. Unscramble these letters to fill in the blanks at the bottom of the page. Then you will have the answer to question. If you need help, read the second chapter of the third book in the New Testament.

1. BASLTE   ◯ _ _ _ _ _

2. ATSR   ◯ _ _ _

3. LNGAES   ◯ _ _ _ _ _

4. PHSDSEHRE   ◯ _ _ _ _ _ _ _ _

5. SMEWNIE   _ ◯ _ _   _ _ _

6. RAYM   ◯ _ _ _

7. OHJPSE   _ _ _ _ _ ◯

8. KDNYEO   _ _ _ _ _ ◯

9. STEXA   ◯ _ _ _ _

10. LMBEHHTEE   _ ◯ _ _ _ _ _ _ _

11. DLGO   _ ◯ _ _

12. RHYMR   _ _ _ ◯ _

13. CRSEIFNAKNNE   _ _ _ _ _ _ _ _ ◯ _ _ _ _

14. UJYONER   _ _ _ ◯ _ _ _

What do all of these words have in common? _ _ _ _ _ _ _ _ _   _ _ _ _ _

48

Bible Window Boxes

The names of Bible characters are hidden in each row of letters in the first column. The second column lists boxes that reveal those names. Think of the rows in the second column as open and closed windows. Only the window boxes with the correct pattern of open and closed windows will reveal the name. To find each name, you need to match the row of letters in the first column with a row of window boxes in the second column. Some have multiple possibilities, but each set of window boxes is only used once. The first one has been done for you.

Hint: If you need help, look in the index of your Bible.

1. D S O A M U L   a.

2. P S A M U I L   b.

3. S N O I A H M   c.

4. F L A U K C E   d.

5. M A R O T Y L   e. **S A U L**

6. J O S H I N T   f.

7. D R E S T A U   g.

8. L B C I O A Z   h.

9. A D M B O S T   i.

10. G A P H A B N   j.

11. R U T D H J Y   k.

12. C O A I S T N   l.

13. A M E B D E L   m.

14. W A D O A C M   n.

Passage Fall

Jesus gave us words to live by and words to give us comfort and hope. The puzzle below will spell a message Jesus gives to all of us. To find it, the letters in each vertical column will "fall" into the squares directly below. However, these letters will not necessarily fall in the order they appear. A black square indicates the end of a word. When you have placed all of the letters in their correct squares, you will be able to read a Bible verse from left to right. The first few have been done for you.

Hint: If you need help, turn to Matthew 6:34.

	R			E				W							
O	W	T	O	I	T	F	O	B		U	T			O	R
O	U	E	R	R	L	O	E	L	F	T	R		N	R	B
T	H	R	R	W	Y	S	R	R	O	D	O	Y	O	A	M
O	W	O	W	I	F	L	A	E	O	R	O	M	T	O	T
T	H	E													

I'm All Mixed Up

In each of the boxes below is hidden the name of a person from a well-known Bible story. To discover the name, take one letter from each column and write it in the space below. The first has been done for you.

Hint: If you need help, look in the index of your Bible.

1.

Ⓓ Ⓐ D D Y
T I Ⓘ Ⓓ
L O Ⓥ E S

D A V I D
_____

2.

E D E N
A T O M
D R A G

_____

3.

M U C H
R O A D
C A T S

_____

4.

S U C H
C O A L
N I L E

_____

5.

E A R
I V Y
T O E

_____

6.

T O A S T
M I L E S
D U S T Y

_____

7.

C O W E R
H A T C H
P E D A L

_____

8.

C A R T S
T O U C H
S T E A M

_____

9.

W A L K
S P U R
T E L L

_____

10.

E X C E E D
A S T H M A
G U I T A R

_____

51

Mixed Up Again

In each of the boxes below is hidden the name of a person from a well-known Bible story. To discover the name, take one letter from each column and write it in the space below.

Hint: If you need help, look in the index of your Bible.

1.

M E E T I N G
C A T C H E S
S W A L L O W

M A T T H E W

2.

C A R E
M I S T
B O O K

_____

3.

C A K E
M U C H
L O S T

_____

4.

M U L E S
T O D A Y
J A U N T

_____

5.

B A S I S
J O I N T
L E M U R

_____

6.

S O H O
J A I L
F E R N

_____

7.

G A R D E N
M O U T H S
A C A D I A

_____

8.

L E M O N
S T R U T
F I N A L

_____

9.

M U C H
B O D Y
P A R T

_____

10.

A S S U R E
B O L T E D
P I N A T A

_____

Our Merciful Lord

Sudoku puzzles are fun and challenging. Use the clues provided to complete this sudoku-style puzzle. Solve the puzzle below using the letters M E R C I F U L. Each letter is used once per block and should be used once per row, both across and down. No letters may be repeated in each row or each block.

Hint: Find the row that spells out *merciful*.

R		L	U				
U	E		M			R	I
L	U			E	F		
		C			F		L
R		E		I		C	
M		U	E				F
U		L			M		R
E	C		R			I	

The Greatest Father of All

Sudoku puzzles are fun and challenging. Use the clues provided to complete this sudoku-style puzzle. Solve the puzzle below using the letters F A T H E R. Each letter is used once per block and should be used once per row, both across and down. No letters may be repeated in each row or each block.

Hint: Find the row that spells out *father*.

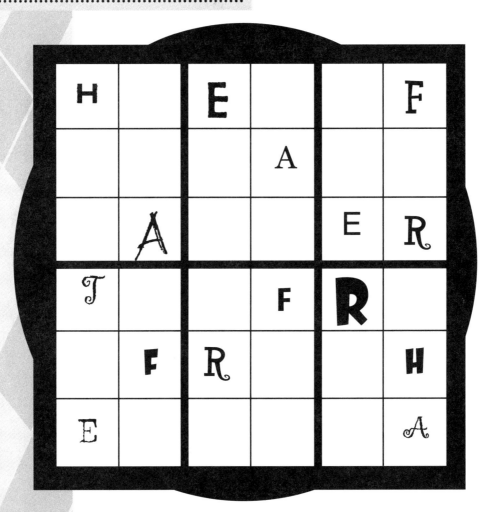

Answers

Fun with Names   page 5

1. Andrew	2. Moses	3. Adam
4. Abel	5. Cain	6. Mark
7. Isaac	8. Sheba	9. Micah
10. Isaiah	11. Esther	12. Aaron

What's Your Name? page 6

1. g	2. k	3. e	4. i
5. c	6. l	7. a	8. m
9. p	10. d	11. j	12. b
13. o	14. h	15. f	16. n

Which Is It? page 7

1. Matthew	2. Ruth	3. Abel	4. Ham
5. Miriam	6. Isaac	7. Martha	8. Baptism
9. Ark	10. Crucifixion	11. Bread	12. Nebuchadnezzar
13. Moses	14. Mary	15. Gold	

Famous Places   page 8

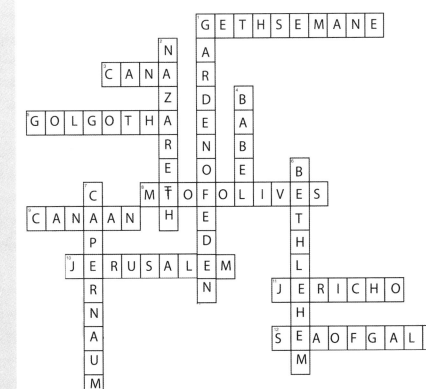

ACROSS:
1. Gethsemane   3. Cana
5. Golgotha   8. Mt. of Olive
9. Canaan   10. Jerusalem
11. Jericho   12. Sea of Galilee

DOWN:
1. Garden of Eden   2. Nazareth
4. Babel   6. Bethlehem
7. Capernaum

Women of the Bible page 9

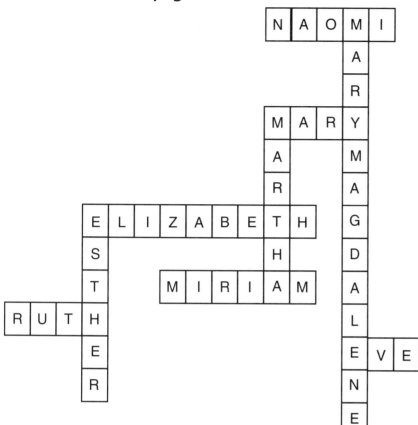

ACROSS:
Naomi
Mary
Elizabeth
Miriam
Eve
Ruth

DOWN:
Mary Magdalene
Martha
Esther

Hidden Disciples page 10

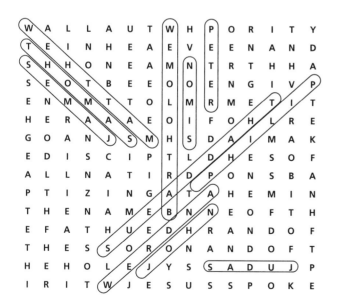

"All authority in heaven and on earth has been given to Me. Therefore go and make disciples of all nations, baptizing them in the name of the Father and of the Son and of the Holy Spirit," [Jesus spoke]. Matthew 28:18–19

It Ends with S page 11

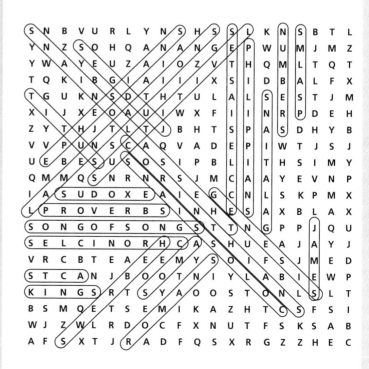

Books of the Bible page 12

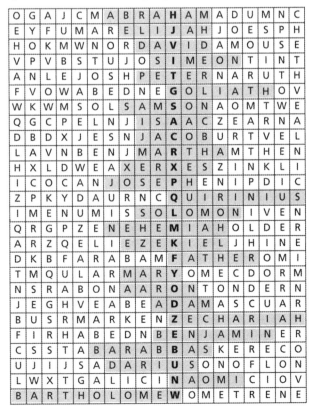

People of the Bible page 13

Pathfinder page 14

Your Word is a lamp to my feet and a light for my path. Psalm 119:105

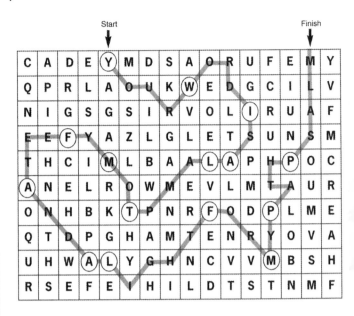

The Path to God page 15

May the Lord answer you when you are in distress. Psalm 20:1

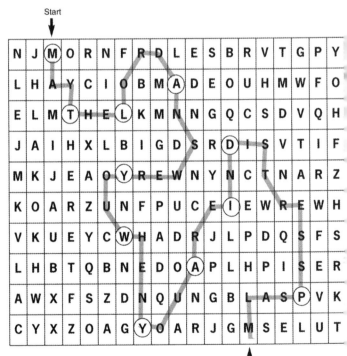

Turn a Verse page 16

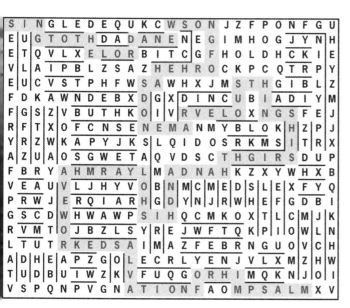

```
S I N G L E D E Q U K C W S O N   J Z F P O N F G U
E U G T O T H D A D A N E N E G I M H O G J Y N H
E T Q V L X E L O R B I T C G F H O L D H C K I E
V L A I P B L Z S A Z H E H R O C K P C Q T R P Y
E U C V S T P H F W S A W H X J M S T H G I B L Z
F D K A W N D E B X D G X D I N C U B I A D I Y M
F G S Z V B U T H K O I V R V E L O X N G S F E J
R F T X O F C N S E N E M A N M Y B L O K H Z P J
Y R Z W K A P Y J K S L Q I D O S R K M S I T R X
A Z U A O S G W E T A Q V D S C T H G I R S D U P
F B R Y A H M R A Y L M A D N A H K Z X Y W H X B
V E A U V L J H Y V O B N M C M E D S L E X F Y Q
P R W J E R Q I A R H G D Y N J R W H E F G D B I
G S C D W H W A W P S I H Q C M K O X T L C M J K
R V M T O J B Z L S Y R E J W F T Q K P I O W L N
L T U T R K E D S A I M A Z F E B R N G U O V C H
A D H E A P Z G O L E C R L Y E N J V L X M Z H W
T U D B U I W Z K J V F U Q G O R H I M Q K N J O I
V S P Q N P V G N A T I O N F A O M P S A L M X V
```

sing to the Lord a new song, for He has done mar-velous things; His right hand and His holy arm have worked salvation for him. Psalm 98:1

Bible Quiz page 17

1. Jesus' birthplace
2. Beginning of creation
3. The story of Daniel
4. The story of Moses
5. Where Jesus prayed before He was crucified
6. Where Jesus was killed on the cross
7. Where Noah's ark came to rest
8. Moses was given the Ten Commandments
9. Jesus was baptized

Categories page 18

Answers may vary, but all should be Bible related.

Find the Relationship   page 19

1. Temptation of Christ
2. Disciples
3. Plagues
4. Beatitudes
5. Old Testament books
6. Story of Joseph
7. Items used in the crucifixion
8. New Testament books
9. Story of Noah
10. Story of the Exodus

Apostle Stumpers page 20

1. Simon (Peter) and Andrew/ James and John
2. Simon
3. Judas
4. Thomas
5. Simon and Andrew
6. Peter
7. Matthew
8. Peter
9. Peter, James, and John
10. James and John
11. Peter
12. Peter, James, and John

What Time Is It? page 21

1. Moses
2. Judas
3. Daniel
4. Mary
5. Elizabeth
6. John the Baptist
7. Isaac
8. Goliath
9. Father or Jehovah
10. Andrew

There is a time for everything, and a season for every activity under heaven. Ecclesiastes 3:1

When Did It Happen?   page 22

"Worship the Lord your God." Luke 4:8

Where Did I Hear That?   page 23

1. Jesus at the temple (Luke 2:49)
2. Birth of Jesus foretold (Luke 1:38)
3. Calling of the disciples (Matthew 4:19)
4. The Last Supper (Luke 22:19)
5. Who is the greatest? (Mark 9:35)
6. The Beatitudes (Matthew 5:3)
7. Jesus walks on the water (Matthew 14:31)
8. The Garden of Gethsemane (Matthew 26:39)
9. Peter disowns Jesus (Matthew 26:34)
10. The death of Jesus (Matthew 27:46)
11. The Great Commission (Matthew 28:19–20)
12. The death of Lazarus (John 11:25)
13. The crucifixion (Luke 23:34)
14. The temptation of Jesus (Matthew 4:4)
15. Angels appear to the shepherds (Luke 2:12)

God's Word Is No Mystery   page 24

But you are a chosen people, a royal priesthood, a holy nation, a people belonging to God, that you may declare the praises of Him who called you out of darkness into His wonderful light.
1 Peter 2:9

Simon Says   page 25

Nebuchadnezzar

It's No Secret   page 26

"Man does not live on bread alone, but on every word that comes from the mouth of God."
Matthew 4:4

What's Left?   page 27

Trust in the Lord with all your heart. Proverbs 3:5

Calling on Jesus   page 28

"I tell you the truth, unless you change and become like little children, you will never enter the kingdom of heaven." Matthew 18:3

Hello, Jesus?   page 29

"Blessed are you who are poor, for yours is the kingdom of God." Luke 6:20

Three of a Kind   page 30

Grace

Biblical Equations   page 31

1. 12 Apostles for Jesus
2. 40 Days and Nights of Rain
3. 3 Crosses on Golgotha
4. 2 of Each Kind of Animal on the Ark
5. 3 Days traveled while Mary and Joseph searched for Jesus
6. 7 Days of Creation
7. 7 Times the Israelites Marched around the City
8. 7 Cities of Revelation
9. 10 Plagues on the Egyptians
10. 10 Commandments on the Tablets

Bits and Pieces   page 32

1. David and Goliath
2. Ruth and Naomi
3. Samson and Delilah
4. Mary and Martha
5. Jacob and Esau
6. Cain and Abel
7. Mary and Joseph
8. Aaron and Moses
9. Peter and John
10. Paul and Silas
11. Abraham and Sarah
12. Daniel and Darius
13. Pharaoh and Moses
14. Jonah and the whale
15. Elisha and Elijah

Christ's Life in Pictures   page 33

1. Miracles
2. Parables
3. Birth
4. Last Supper
5. Ascension
6. Transfiguration
7. Crucifixion
8. Temptation
9. Gethsemane
10. Baptism
11. Resurrection

Picture Books   page 34

1. Matthew
2. Numbers
3. Exodus
4. Acts
5. Joshua
6. Mark
7. Genesis
8. John
9. Corinthians
10. Deuteronomy
11. Luke
12. Leviticus

Number Block   page 35

Here is one possible answer.

30	4	2	4	40
4	3	2	1	10
2	1	1	3	7
4	2	2	4	12
40	10	7	12	

Proverb Wheel 1   page 36

1. Sheep's
2. Reason
3. Health
4. Adorns
5. Create
6. Freely
7. Cherub
8. Proved
9. Breath

The eyes of the Lord are everywhere. Proverbs 15:3

Proverb Wheel 2   page 37

1. Whiter
2. Guards
3. Shrewd
4. Listen
5. Guides
6. Desire
7. Silver
8. Prefer
9. Lovers

He who guards his lips guards his life. Proverbs 13:3

What's Missing?   page 38

1. Moses
2. Noah
3. Daniel
4. Mary
5. Adam
6. Eve
7. Samuel
8. Joseph
9. Jesus
10. David
11. Elijah
12. Ruth
13. Naomi
14. Solomon
15. Abraham
16. Isaac
17. Andrew

Total number of O's=7
Total number of A's=15
Total number of U's=3
Total number of E's=9
Total number of I's=5
Number of books in the Old Testament=39

Where Am I?   page 39

1. Galilee
2. Jericho
3. Jerusalem
4. Bethlehem
5. Babylon
6. Samaria
7. Nazareth
8. Damascus
9. Cana
10. Emmaus

Who Am I?   page 40

1. David
2. Goliath
3. Adam
4. Eve
5. Ruth
6. Moses
7. Noah
8. Jesus
9. Peter
10. Judas
11. Naomi
12. Esther

Put Them All Together and What Have You Got?   page 41

Genesis
Galatians
Joshua
Habakkuk
Exodus
Isaiah
Philemon
Hosea
Chronicles
Malachi
Ephesians
Colossians
Timothy

Six-Letter Words   page 42

1. Christ	2. Garden	3. Donkey
4. Father	5. Angels	6. Andrew
7. Anoint	8. Church	9. Chosen
10. Elisha	11. Gospel	12. Heaven
13. Israel	14. Joseph	15. Palace
16. Redeem	17. Refuge	18. Sacred
19. Samuel	20. Savior	21. Sorrow
22. Spirit	23. Thomas	24. Virtue

Disciples in Christ   Page 43

Answers will vary.

Little Words from Big Words page 44

Old Testament

1. Lamentations	2. Nehemiah
3. Leviticus or Exodus	4. Esther
5. Proverbs	6. Hosea
7. Haggai	8. Nahum

New Testament

1. Romans	2. Matthew
3. Timothy	4. Thessalonians
5. Philippians	6. Mark
7. Colossians	8. Philemon
9. Revelation	10. Ephesians
11. James	12. Hebrews

Mystery Code to Jesus' Life page 45

1. Transfiguration	2. Last Supper
3. Birth	4. Crucifixion
5. Baptism	6. Temptation
7. Sermon on the Mount	8. Miracles
9. Parables	10. Gethsemane
11. Resurrection	12. Ascension

Scrambled Books   page 46

1. Hosea	2. Obadiah
3. Genesis	4. Malachi
5. Leviticus	6. Zechariah
7. Deuteronomy	8. Isaiah
9. Zephaniah	10. Ezekiel
11. Nehemiah	12. Exodus
13. Joshua	14. Ecclesiastes
15. Jeremiah	16. Habakkuk
17. Lamentations	

And It Was Good   page 47

1. Day	2. Plants	3. Stars	4. Man
5. Night	6. Moon	7. Sky	8. Woman
9. Animals	10. Heavens	11. Sun	12. Earth
13. Oceans			

Creation story

The Greatest Birth   page 48

1. Stable	2. Star	3. Angels
4. Shepherds	5. Wise Men	6. Mary
7. Joseph	8. Donkey	9. Taxes
10. Bethlehem	11. Gold	12. Myrrh
13. Frankincense	14. Journey	

Christmas story

Bible Window Boxes   page 49

1. e (Saul)	2. i (Paul)	3. a (Noah)
4. m (Luke)	5. f (Mary)	6. j (John)
7. d (Esau)	8. h (Boaz)	9. n (Amos)
10. b (Ahab)	11. l (Ruth)	12. g (Cain)
13. k (Abel)	14. c (Adam)	

Passage Fall   page 50

"Therefore do not worry about tomorrow, for tomorrow will worry about itself."
Matthew 6:34

I'm All Mixed Up   page 51

1. David	2. Adam	3. Ruth	4. Noah
5. Eve	6. Moses	7. Peter	8. Sarah
9. Saul	10. Esther		

Mixed Up Again   page 52

1. Matthew   2. Mark   3. Luke   4. Judas
5. Jesus   6. John   7. Martha   8. Simon
9. Mary   10. Pilate

Our Merciful Lord   page 53

F	R	I	L	U	C	M	E
C	U	E	F	M	L	R	I
L	I	U	M	R	E	F	C
M	**E**	**R**	**C**	**I**	**F**	**U**	**L**
R	L	M	E	F	I	C	U
I	M	C	U	E	R	L	F
U	F	L	I	C	M	E	R
E	C	F	R	L	U	I	M

The Greatest Father of All   page 54

H	T	E	R	A	F
R	E	F	A	H	T
F	**A**	**T**	**H**	**E**	**R**
T	H	A	F	R	E
A	F	R	E	T	H
E	R	H	T	F	A